Acknowledgements

The compilers and publisher wish to thank the following for their kind permission to reproduce poems:

A Small Dragon
George Allen & Unwin for 'A Small Dragon' by Brian Patten from *Notes to the Hurrying Man*; Ian Serraillier for 'St Brendan and the Fishes' from *The Windmill Book of Ballads*, published by Heinemann Educational Books; Macmillan Administration Basingstoke Ltd for 'The Sweet-tooth' by Wilfrid Wilson Gibson from *Collected Poems 1905–1925* and 'The Shell', 'Midnight' and 'The Centaurs' by James Stephens from *Collected Poems*; The Society of Authors as the literary representative of the Estate of John Masefield for a passage from 'The Everlasting Mercy'; Hal Summers for 'Wet Through'; Charles Causley for 'Colonel Fazackerley' from *Figgie Hobbin* published by Macmillan; James Kirkup for 'The Zebra', 'The Shepherd's Tale' translated from Raoul Ponchon's poem in French, and 'Cows'; the Estate of A. S. J. Tessimond for 'A Hot Day' from *Not Love Perhaps* published by Autolycus Press; D. J. Enright for 'Better Be Kind to Them Now' from *Rhyme Times Rhyme* published by Chatto & Windus Ltd; Edward Lowbury for 'The Roc' from *Green Magic*; Dobson Books Ltd for 'Time for Bed' from *Four Seasons* by Leonard Clark; Edward Arnold (Publishers) Ltd for 'Ruthless Rhyme One' from *Most Ruthless Rhymes for Heartless Homes* by Harry Graham; the Estate of the late Ogden Nash for 'An Introduction to Dogs' from *Family Reunion* published by J. M. Dent; Anthony Thwaite for 'At Dunwich' from *The Stones of Emptiness*; Sidgwick & Jackson Ltd for 'India' by W. J. Turner.

'Blackberry-Picking' from *Death of a Naturalist* by Seamus Heaney, 'The Serpent' by Theodore Roethke from *The Collected Poems of Theodore Roethke* and 'Glass Falling' by Louis Macneice from *The Collected Poems of Louis Macneice* are all reprinted by permission of Faber and Faber Ltd. 'The Serpent' is also copyright © 1950 by Theodore Roethke from *The Collected Poems of Theodore Roethke*. Reprinted by permission of Doubleday & Company, Inc. 'An Introduction to Dogs' is copyright 1938 by Ogden Nash. Reprinted from *The Face is Familiar* by permission of Little, Brown and Co.

King Foo Foo
Charles Causley for 'King Foo Foo' from *Figgie Hobbin* published by Macmillan; Edward Arnold (Publishers) Ltd for 'Ruthless Rhymes Two and Three' from *Most Ruthless Rhymes for Heartless Homes* by Harry Graham; Mrs A. M. Walsh for 'First Dip' by John Walsh; James Kirkup for 'The Redbreast'; André Deutsch for 'Apples' by Laurie Lee from *My Many-Coated Man*; Barrie & Jenkins for 'Three Cheers for the Black, White and Blue' by Ruth Pitter from *Poems 1926–1966*; Mrs H. M. Davies for 'A Dream of Winter' from *The Complete Poems of W. H. Davies* published by Jonathan Cape; Dobson Books Ltd for 'Pebbles' from *Four Seasons* by Leonard Clark and 'Fishers' from *Collected Poems and Verses for Children* by Leonard Clark; Ian Serraillier for 'The Hen and the Carp' from *The Weaver Birds* published by Macmillan; Basil Blackwell for 'The Ballad of the Carpenters' by L. A. G. Strong from *The Lowery Road*; Jenny Joseph for 'Warning' from *Rose in the Afternoon*; Warren House Press for 'Night Fears' by Brian Hill from *Collected Poems and Translations*; Jacques Prévert for 'How to Paint the Portrait of a Bird' from *The Fern in the Rock* by Paul Dehn published by Hamish Hamilton.

'On a Quay by the Sea' from *Runes and Rhymes, Tunes and Chimes* by George Barker and 'Follower' from *Death of a Naturalist* by Seamus Heaney are reprinted by permission of Faber and Faber Ltd. 'Night Clouds' is from *The Complete Poetical Works of Amy Lowell*. Copyright 1955 by Houghton Mifflin Company. Reprinted by permission of the publisher.

The Flattered Flying Fish
Richard Rieu for 'The Flattered Flying Fish' by E. V. Rieu; Edward Lowbury for 'The Monster' and 'The Storm' from *Green Magic*; Philip Hobsbaum for 'House of Sand'; Edward Arnold (Publishers) Ltd for 'Ruthless Rhymes Four and Five' from *Most Ruthless Rhymes for Heartless Homes* by Harry Graham; the Literary Trustees of Walter de la Mare and The Society of Authors as their representative for 'Kiph' and 'The Song of Seven' by Walter de la Mare; The Society of Authors as the literary representative of the Estate of John Masefield for a passage from 'Reynard the Fox' by John Masefield; The Hogarth Press for 'Fetching Cows' by Norman McCaig from *Measures*; Robert Graves for 'I Wonder What It Feels Like to be Drowned' from *Fairies and Fusiliers* published by William Heinemann Ltd; Dobson Books Ltd for 'Boy and Fish' from *Collected Poems and Verses for Children* by Leonard Clark; Macmillan, London and Basingstoke, for 'Parrot' from *Brownjohn's Beasts* by Alan Brownjohn; James Kirkup for 'The Riddle of Christmas' and 'Words for Singing'; The Acorn Press for 'The Squirrel' by Sylvia Read from *The Poetical Ark*; Sidgwick & Jackson Ltd for 'Romance' by W. J. Turner; William Heinemann Ltd for 'Brave Rover' from *Max in Verse* by Max Beerbohm; D. J. Enright for 'The Old Field' from *Rhyme Times Rhyme* published by Chatto & Windus Ltd; Sir Herbert Read for 'Carol' from *Moon's Farm* published by Faber and Faber Ltd.

'Apartment Cats' is reprinted by permission of Faber and Faber Ltd from *Moly* by Thom Gunn. 'A Garden at Night' is from *The Blackbird in the Lilac* by James Reeves published by Oxford University Press 1952. Reprinted by permission of the publisher. 'Goodbat Nightman' by Roger McGough is from *Penguin Modern Poets: No 10*. Copyright © 1967 by Roger McGough. 'A shadow is floating through the moonlight' from Randall Jarrell, *The Bat Poet* (Kestrel Books, 1977), p. 12, © 1963, 1964 by Macmillan Publishing Co. Inc. Reprinted by permission of Penguin Books Ltd and Macmillan Publishing Co. Inc.

ROUND ABOUT
TEN

poems for today

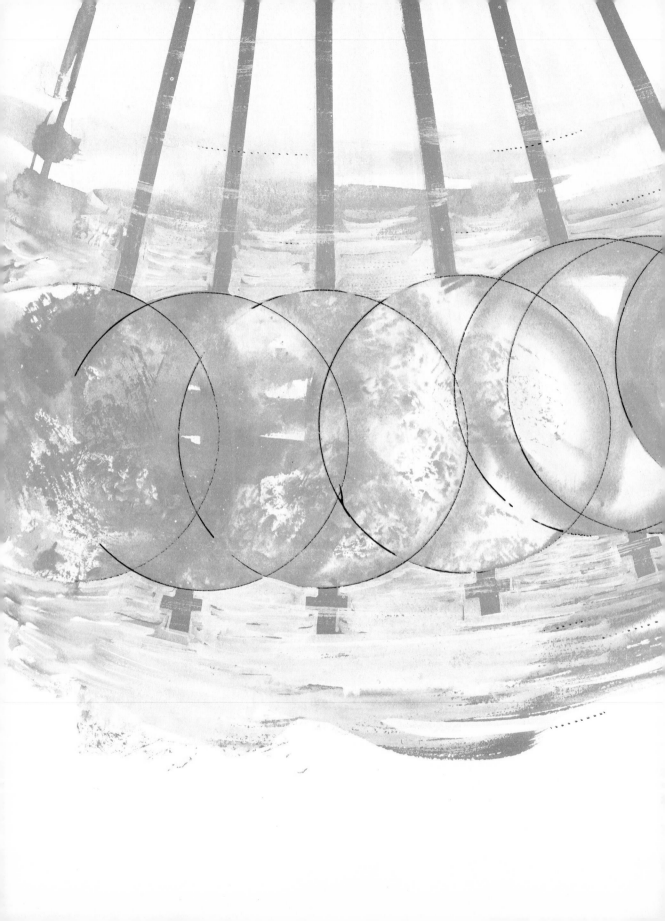

Round about ten

poems for today

selected by Geoffrey Palmer & Noel Lloyd

with illustrations by Denis Wrigley

FREDERICK WARNE

For Barbara and Danny Middlebrook,
and David Alexander Clow

Published by Frederick Warne (Publishers) Ltd, London

© Frederick Warne (Publishers) Ltd, London, 1979

ISBN 0 7232 2358 0

Printed in Great Britain by Butler and Tanner Ltd,
Frome and London

1252.679

Contents

A Small Dragon

Contents

A Small Dragon

I've found a small dragon in the woodshed.
Think it must have come from deep inside a forest
because it's damp and green and leaves
are still reflecting in its eyes.

I fed it on many things, tried grass,
the roots of stars, hazel-nut and dandelion,
but it stared up at me as if to say, I need
foods you can't provide.

It made a nest among the coal,
not unlike a bird's but larger,
it is out of place here
and is quite silent.

If you believed in it I would come
hurrying to your house to let you share my wonder,
but I want instead to see
if you yourself will pass this way.

BRIAN PATTEN

St Brendan and the Fishes

St Brendan chanted mass in voyage
over the sabbath-quiet sea,
and seven frail land-longing brothers
    listened fearfully.

'Master, sing lower! Monsters
under our keel fiercely fly.
If you anger them with chanting, we
    must surely die.'

St Brendan laughed loud: 'O Lord,
have pity on Thy wayward sheep!'
In answer four creatures zoomed
    up from the deep—

Agg the sea-cat, inveterate in wiles,
Puff the Angel, like a pillow,
Old Whacker the whale and
Moon-splinter, minnow.

On wobble knees the brothers watched
four perils nibble at the rudder.
'Lord Jesus, hinder these fish or find them
    other fodder!'

But they for joy of Paul's Feast
made merry with water sport
and fun frolic, doing the voyagers
    no hurt,

till, high song over, St Brendan
said, 'Fish, that's all for today.'
In wave-scrubble tails wiggle and fluke,
    flick and away—

Agg the sea-cat, inveterate in wiles,
Puff the Angel, like a pillow,
Old Whacker the whale and
Moon-splinter, minnow.

IAN SERRAILLIER

The Sweet-tooth

Taking a turn after tea
Through orchards of Mirabellea,
Where clusters of yellow and red
Dangled and glowed overhead,
Who should I see
But old Timothy,
Hale and hearty as hearty can be—
Timothy under the crab-apple tree.

His blue eyes twinkling at me,
Munching and crunching with glee,
And wagging his wicked old head,
I've still got a sweet tooth,
        he said—
A hundred and three
Come January,
I've got one tooth left in my head,
        said he,
Timothy under the crab-apple tree.

WILFRID GIBSON

from The Everlasting Mercy

I told a tale, to Jim's delight,
Of where the tom-cats go by night,
And how when moonlight come they went
Among the chimneys, black and bent,
From roof to roof, from house to house,
With little baskets full of mouse
All red and white, both joint and chop;
Like meat out of a butcher's shop;
Then all along the wall they creep
And everyone is fast asleep,
And honey-hunting moths go by,
And the bread-batch crickets cry;
Then on they hurry, never waiting,
To lawyer's backyard cellar grating,
Where Jaggard's cat, with clever paw,
Unhooks a broke-brick's secret door;
Then down into the cellar black,
Across the wood-slug's slimy track,
Into an old cask's quiet hollow,
Where they've got seats for what's to follow,
Then each tom-cat lights little candles,
And O, the stories and the scandals,
And O, the songs and Christmas carols,
And O, the milk from little barrels.
They light a fire fit for toasting
(And how good mouse-meat smells when roasting),
Then down they sit to merry feast
When moon goes west and sun comes east.

JOHN MASEFIELD

Wet Through

Being now completely wet through to the skin
I begin to see I was a fool to mind it.
This that wets me, what is it but good rain
That has left half England growing greener behind it?

The trees are drunk with it; the greedy grasses
Hold up their infinitesimal hands to catch it;
The pools to hold it break their looking-glasses
And the ditch runs with a stormy noise to match it.

This cloud like a tanker or rich merchantman
Has come from far, with the great wind that fans it,
And over Exmoor or Cotswold it began
To unload its precious freight, after long transit.

Then eastward over the shires it took its tour
By Avon and by Thames, by Test and Kennet,
By Arun and by Ouse, Medway and Stour,
Pouring such wealth, the earth cannot contain it.

And now like medieval pilgrims or
Sturdy Elizabethan beggars, I,
Wet to the skin, look up, and see the core
Of darkness rent in golden rags on high.

The last drops fall, the riddled pools resume
Their smooth reflections; only the hidden freshet
Is loud still, running in the tunnelled gloom
Where strawberry, sloe, and bramble shoots enmesh it.

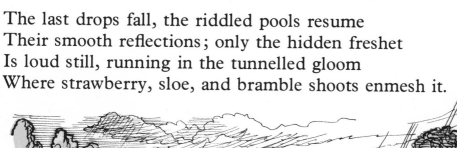

Outpacing me, the enormous cloud steams on,
Its hold still heavy-laden, its hull black,
And leaves a world new-minted; even the sun
Seems washed, and with adored heat burns my back.

HAL SUMMERS

Colonel Fazackerley

Colonel Fazackerley Butterworth-Toast
Bought an old castle complete with a ghost,
But someone or other forgot to declare
To Colonel Fazack that the spectre was there.

On the very first evening, while waiting to dine,
The Colonel was taking a fine sherry wine,
When the ghost, with a furious flash and a flare,
Shot out of the chimney and shivered, 'Beware!'

Colonel Fazackerley put down his glass
And said, 'My dear fellow, that's really first class!
I just can't conceive how you do it at all.
I imagine you're going to a Fancy Dress Ball?'

At this, the dread ghost gave a withering cry.
Said the Colonel (his monocle firm in his eye),
'Now just how you do it I wish I could think.
Do sit down and tell me, and please have a drink.'

The ghost in his phosphorous cloak gave a roar
And floated about between ceiling and floor.
He walked through a wall and returned through a pane
And backed up the chimney and came down again.

Said the Colonel, 'With laughter I'm feeling quite weak!'
(As trickles of merriment ran down his cheek).
'My house-warming party I hope you won't spurn.
You *must* say you'll come and you'll give us a turn!'

At this, the poor spectre—quite out of his wits—
Proceeded to shake himself almost to bits.
He rattled his chains and he clattered his bones
And he filled the whole castle with mumbles and moans.

But Colonel Fazackerley, just as before,
Was simply delighted and called out, 'Encore!'
At which the ghost vanished, his efforts in vain,
And never was seen at the castle again.

'Oh dear, what a pity!' said Colonel Fazack.
'I don't know his name, so I can't call him back.'
And then with a smile that was hard to define,
Colonel Fazackerley went in to dine.

CHARLES CAUSLEY

Triolet

Here's a little New Year pitched out of the sky
  With a great bag of mystery under his arm,
At the World's street-door he's beginning to cry,
(Here's a little New Year pitched out of the sky)
Let's take him in out of the cold, and pry
  In the bag, while he sits by the fire to warm.
Here's a little New Year pitched out of the sky
  With a great bag of mystery under his arm!

FR ROLFE

The Zebra

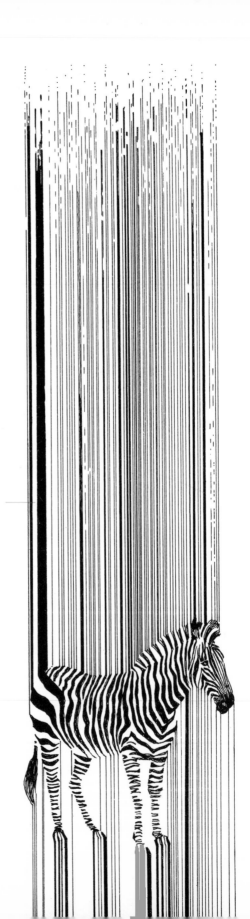

Zany
pit pony
fenced in the
open
prison of stripes—

bodypainted
with brushes
of black
or white—

skintight
bodystocking

smoothed op
art into ribs

upon ribs
and rings

upon tail
and shawls

upon shoulder
and masks

upon head
and gills

upon flank
and rills

upon back
and furrows

on forehead
and wrinkles

on neck
on ankles—

Zany
pit pony
fenced in the
locked
prison of stripes.

JAMES KIRKUP

A Hot Day

Cottonwool clouds loiter.
A lawnmower, very far,
Birrs. Then a bee comes
To a crimson rose and softly,
Deftly and fatly crams
A velvet body in.

A tree, June-lazy, makes
A tent of dim green light.
Sunlight weaves in the leaves,
Honey-light laced with leaf-light,
Green interleaved with gold.
Sunlight gathers its rays
In sheaves, which the wind unweaves
And then reweaves—the wind
That puffs a smell of grass
Through the heat-heavy, trembling
Summer pool of air.

A. S. J. TESSIMOND

Better Be Kind to Them Now

A squirrel is digging up the bulbs
In half the time Dad took to bury them.

A small dog is playing football
With a mob of boys. He beats them all,
Scoring goals at both ends.
A kangaroo would kick the boys as well.

Birds are so smart they can drink milk
Without removing the bottle-top.

Cats stay clean, and never have to be
Carried screaming to the bathroom.
They don't get their heads stuck in railings,
They negotiate first with their whiskers.

The gecko walks on the ceiling, and
The cheetah can outrun the Royal Scot.
The lion cures his wounds by licking them,
And the guppy has fifty babies at a go.

The cicada plays the fiddle for hours on end,
And a man-size flea could jump over St Paul's.

If ever these beasts should get together
Then we are done for, children.
I don't much fancy myself as a python's pet,
But it might come to that!

D. J. ENRIGHT

The Shepherd's Tale

Woman, you'll never credit what
  My two eyes saw this night ...
But first of all we'll have a drop,
  It's freezing now, all right.

It was the queerest going-on
  That I did e'er behold:
A holy child out in the barn,
  A baby all in gold.

Now let's get started on the soup,
  And let me tell it you,
For though there's not a thing made up,
  It still seems hardly true.

There he was laid upon the straw,
  Will you dish up the stew?
The ass did bray, the hens did craw,
  I'll have some cabbage too.

First there was a king from Prussia,
  At least that's how he looked,
Then there was the king of Russia.
  This stew's been overcooked.

There they were kneeling on the ground.
  Come, have a bite to eat.
First I just stared and stood around.
  Have just a taste of meat!

Well, one of them he ups and says
  A long speech—kind of funny.
Here, what about that last new cheese,
  Is it still runny?

The little 'un, wise as wise could be,
    Just didn't care for that.
But he was pleased as punch with me
    When I took off me hat.

I took his little fists in mine,
    In front of all those nobs.
Fetch us a jug of our best wine
    My dear, we'll wet our gobs.

That very instant, as if I'd
    Had a good swig of drink,
I felt a great warm joy inside,
    But why, I cannot think.

Ah, this wine's the stuff, by Mary!
    When he's grown up a bit,
That little fellow, just you see,
    He shall have some of it!

We might have all been knelt there yet,
    Put a Yule log on the fire,
But suddenly he starts to fret—
    He'd begun to tire.

Then 'Sirs', his mother she did say,
   'It grieves me to remind
You that it's time to go away
   When you have been so kind.

'But see, how sleepy he's become,
   He's crying, let him rest.
You all know how to find our home
   Each one's a welcome guest.'

And so in silence we went out,
   But the funniest thing—
Those three fine kings, so rich and stout,
   Did wish me good-morning!

You see, love, that's how it began.
   The God born on the earth
This night's no ordinary one.
   Let's celebrate his birth!

RAOUL PONCHON
(Translated from the French by James Kirkup)

from Autumn

No more the fields with scatter'd grain supply
The restless wandering tenants of the sty;
From oak to oak they run with eager haste,
And wrangling share the first delicious taste
Of fallen acorns; yet but thinly found
Till the strong gale has shook them to the ground.
The trudging sow leads forth her numerous young,
Playful, and white, and clean, the briars among,

Till briars and thorns increasing fence them round,
Where last year's mould'ring leaves bestrew the ground,
And o'er their heads, loud lash'd by furious squalls,
Bright from their cups the rattling treasure falls.
Whole days and nights they tarry midst their store,
Nor quit the woods till oaks can yield no more.

ROBERT BLOOMFIELD

The Shell

And then I pressed the shell
Close to my ear,
And listened well.

And straightway, like a bell,
Came low and clear
The slow, sad, murmur of far distant seas

Whipped by an icy breeze
Upon a shore
Wind-swept and desolate.

It was a sunless strand that never bore
The footprint of a man,
Nor felt the weight

Since time began
Of any human quality or stir,
Save what the dreary winds and waves incur.

And in the hush of waters was the sound
Of pebbles, rolling round;
For ever rolling, with a hollow sound:

And bubbling sea-weeds, as the waters go,
Swish to and fro
Their long cold tentacles of slimy grey:

There was no day;
Nor ever came a night
Setting the stars alight

To wonder at the moon:
Was twilight only, and the frightened croon,
Smitten to whimpers, of the dreary wind

And waves that journeyed blind . . .
And then I loosed my ear—Oh, it was sweet
To hear a cart go jolting down the street.

JAMES STEPHENS

The Roc

Scattered like flotsam on the erupting sea
   When the ship cracked, Sinbad and his sailors
     Gasped for air, clung to the planks and oars,
Then struggled madly for the beach. Some three
Who managed to escape the crags were thrown
   On yellow sand, and fell asleep at once,
     Soaked through but too exhausted to take shelter,
And slept like dead men till next day at noon.

On waking, someone noticed a black cloud
   Descending over them, like a huge raven
      With curved bill, wings, extended talons,
And voice of thunder, distant but quite loud.
Sinbad grew pale, trembled and shouted, 'Quick,
   Find shelter somewhere; this is the great Roc,
      The bird of prey with wingspan of a mile!
Run to that cave; don't stop to have a look!'

They reached the grotto just in time,—the sky
   Had grown pitch-black, the wingbeats were a gale;
      But, safe in hiding, Sinbad laughed: 'A miracle!
It's not the Roc that's huge, but you and I,
My sailors, who are small, and growing smaller;
   Soon we'll be microscopic, and that crow—
      As harmless as a lion to a gnat—
Won't even notice when we choose to go.'

EDWARD LOWBURY

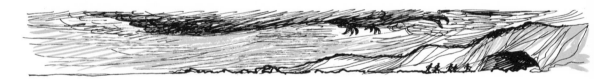

Sea Urchins

Sea urchins:
         vicious black spiked globes
lurking in crannies of rocks,
waiting for human arms or legs
in which to thrust their needle darts.

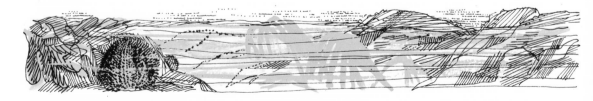

Sea urchins:
> sleek black-haired boys,
shiny bodies done to a sun's turn
flying through the genial air
as they dive arrow-swift into
the rumpled sea—
eardrums and lungs taut, searching for

sea urchins:
> vicious black spiked globes
prised out, trapped, made harmless by

sea urchins:
> sleek black-haired boys

NOEL LLOYD

The Water Lilies

The water lilies, white and yellow flowers,
  How beautiful they are upon the lake!
I've stood and looked upon the place for hours,
  And thought how fine a garden they would make.
The pleasant leaves upon the water float;
  The dragon-fly would come and stay for hours,
And when the water pushed the pleasure boat,
  Would find a safer place among the flowers.
They lay like Pleasure in a quiet place,
  Close where the moor-hen loved her nest to make,—
They lay like Beauty with a smiling face,
  And I have called them 'Ladies of the Lake!'
I've brought the longest pole and stood for hours,
And tried for years, before I got those flowers!

JOHN CLARE

Time for Bed

Bedtime. Who said it?
I did not hear, sun
still there, no bats flit
around the house, only one
small star lodged up in the sky,
my day's not done.
I'd rather wait, sit
here by the window, stay
at ease with you until
birdsong and summer light
fade in the distance right away,
little creatures of the night
come out with shadows on the hill.
Bedtime. I'm coming soon,
no need for any voice to call,
no hurry yet, the moon
is still the clock for all
who turn to sleep,
so let her slowly rise
out of the cloudy deep;
and long before I close my eyes,
give up counting sheep,
she will be shining overhead,
and I in time for bed.

LEONARD CLARK

Midnight

And suddenly I wakened in a fright;
I thought I heard a movement in the room
But did not dare to look; I snuggled right
Down underneath the bedclothes—Then a boom,
And a tremendous voice said, '*Sit up, lad,*
And let me see your face.' So up I sat,
Although I didn't want to—

I was glad
I did though, for it was an angel that
Had called me, and he said, he'd come to know
Was I the boy who wouldn't say his prayers
Nor do his sums—and that I'd have to go
Straight down to hell because of such affairs:

... I said I'd be converted, and do good
If he would let me off—He said he would.

JAMES STEPHENS

Ruthless Rhyme One

Auntie, did you feel no pain
Falling from that apple-tree?
Will you do it, please, again?
'Cos my friend here didn't see.

HARRY GRAHAM

Cows

In buttercup and daisy fields
The lowing cattle, white and brown,
Lie by the creamy hedge of may,
Or up to their shoulders stand
In waves of clovered hay.

Under the pasture's trees that grow
Out of their own dark pools of green
They gather in the evening's pale
Summerhouse of sky and leaves,
And milk the shadows of the brindled vale.

JAMES KIRKUP

Blackberry-Picking

Late August, given heavy rain and sun
For a full week, the blackberries would ripen.
At first, just one, a glossy purple clot
Among others, red, green, hard as a knot.
You ate that first one and its flesh was sweet
Like thickened wine: summer's blood was in it
Leaving stains upon the tongue and lust for
Picking. Then red ones inked up and that hunger
Sent us out with milk-cans, pea-tins, jam-pots
Where briars scratched and wet grass bleached our boots.
Round hayfields, cornfields and potato-drills
We trekked and picked until the cans were full,
Until the tinkling bottom had been covered
With green ones, and on the top big dark blobs burned
Like a plate of eyes. Our hands were peppered
With thorn pricks, our palms sticky as Bluebeard's.

We hoarded the fresh berries in the byre.
But when the bath was filled we found a fur,
A rat-grey fungus, glutting on our cache.
The juice was stinking too. Once off the bush
The fruit fermented, the sweet flesh would turn sour.
I always felt like crying. It wasn't fair
That all the lovely canfuls smelt of rot.
Each year I hoped they'd keep, knew they would not.

SEAMUS HEANEY

23

At Dunwich

Fifteen churches lie here
Under the North Sea;
Forty-five years ago
The last went down the cliff.
You can see, at low tide,
A mound of masonry
Chewed like a damp bun.

In the village now (if you call
Dunwich a village now,
With a handful of houses, one street,
And a shack for Tizer and tea),
You can ask an old man
To show you the stuff they've found
On the beach when there's been a storm:

Knife-blades, buckles and rings,
Enough coins to fill an old sock,
Badges that men wore
When they'd been on pilgrimage,
Armfuls of broken pots.
People cut bread, paid cash,
Buttoned up against the cold.

Fifteen churches, and men
In thousands working at looms,
And wives brewing up stews
In great grey cooking-pots.
I put out a hand and pull
A sherd from the cliff's jaws.
The sand trickles, then falls.

Nettles grow on the cliffs
In clumps as high as a house.
The houses have gone away.
Stand and look at the sea
Eating the land as it walks
Steadily treading the tops
Of fifteen churches' spires.

ANTHONY THWAITE

India

They hunt, the velvet tigers in the jungle,
The spotted jungle full of shapeless patches—
Sometimes they're leaves, sometimes they're hanging flowers,
Sometimes they're hot gold patches of the sun:
They hunt, the velvet tigers in the jungle.

What do they hunt by glimmering pools of water,
By the round silver Moon, the Pool of Heaven?—
In the striped grass, amid the barkless trees—
The stars scattered like eyes of beasts above them!

What do they hunt, their hot breath scorching insects?
Insects that blunder blindly in the way,
Vividly fluttering—they also are hunting,
Are glittering with a tiny ecstasy!

The grass is flaming and the trees are growing,
The very mud is gurgling in the pools,
Green toads are watching, crimson parrots flying,
Two pairs of eyes meet one another glowing—
They hunt, the velvet tigers in the jungle.

W. J. TURNER

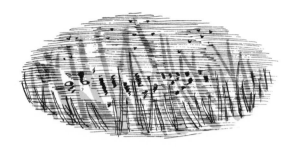

Morning

The morning wakens with the lumping flails,
Chilly and cold; the early-rising clown
Hurkles along and blows his finger nails;
Icicles from the cottage eaves hang down,
Which peeping children wish for in their play.
The field, once clad in autumn's russet brown,
Spreads from the eye its circle far away
In one huge sheet of snow; from the white wood
The crows all silent seek the dreary fens,
And starnels blacken through the air in crowds;
The sheep stand bleating in their turnip pen
And loathe their frozen food; while labouring men
Button their coats more close from angry clouds
And wish for night and its snug fire agen.

JOHN CLARE

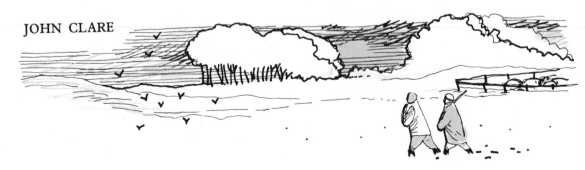

The Serpent

There was a Serpent who had to sing.
There was. There was.
He simply gave up Serpenting.
Because. Because.
He didn't like his Kind of Life;
He couldn't find a proper Wife;
He was a Serpent with a soul;
He got no Pleasure down his Hole.
And so, of course, he had to Sing,
And Sing he did, like Anything!
The Birds, they were, they were Astounded;
And various Measures Propounded
To stop the Serpent's Awful Racket:
They bought a Drum. He wouldn't Whack it.
They sent—you always send—to Cuba
And got a Most Commodious Tuba;
They got a Horn, they got a Flute,
But Nothing would suit.
He said, 'Look, Birds, all this is futile:
I do *not* like to Bang or Tootle.'
And then he cut loose with a Horrible Note
That practically split the Top of his Throat.
'You see,' he said, with a Serpent's Leer,
'I'm Serious about my Singing Career!'
And the Woods Resounded with many a Shriek
As the Birds flew off to the End of Next Week.

THEODORE ROETHKE

The Centaurs

Playing upon the hill three centaurs were!
They lifted each a hoof! They stared at me!
And stamped the dust!

They stamped the dust! They snuffed upon the air!
And all their movements had the fierce glee
Of power, and pride, and lust!

Of power and pride and lust! Then, with a shout,
They tossed their heads, and wheeled, and galloped round,
In furious brotherhood!

In furious brotherhood! Around, about,
They charged, they swerved, they leaped! Then, bound on bound,
They raced into the wood!

JAMES STEPHENS

28

Sonnet to Winter

A wrinkled, crabbèd man they picture thee,
Old Winter, with a rugged beard as grey
As the long moss upon the apple-tree;
Blue-lipt, an ice-drop at thy sharp blue nose,
Close muffled up, and on thy dreary way,
Plodding alone through sleet and drifting snows.
They should have drawn thee by the high-heapt hearth,
Old Winter! seated in the great arm'd chair,
Watching the children at their Christmas mirth;
Or circled by them as thy lips declare
Some merry jest or tale of murder dire,
Or troubled spirit that disturbs the night,
Pausing at times to rouse the mouldering fire,
Or taste the old October* brown and bright.

*ale brewed in October

ROBERT SOUTHEY

An Introduction to Dogs

The dog is man's best friend.
He has a tail on one end.
Up in front he has teeth.
And four legs underneath.

Dogs like to bark.
They like it best after dark.
They not only frighten prowlers away
But also hold the sandman at bay.

A dog that is indoors
To be let out implores.
You let him out and what then?
He wants back in again.

Dogs display reluctance and wrath
If you try to give them a bath.
They bury bones in hideaways
And half the time they trot sideaways.

They cheer up people who are frowning,
And rescue people who are drowning,
They also track mud on beds,
And chew people's clothes to shreds.

Dogs in the country have fun.
They run and run and run.
But in the city this species
Is dragged around on leashes.

Dogs are upright as a steeple
And much more loyal than people.
Well people may be reprehensibler
But that's probably because they are sensibler.

OGDEN NASH

Glass Falling

The glass is going down. The sun
Is going down. The forecasts say
It will be warm, with frequent showers.
We ramble down the showery hours
And amble up and down the day.
Mary will wear her black goloshes
And splash the puddles on the town;
And soon on fleets of mackintoshes
The rain is coming down, the frown
Is coming down of heaven showing
A wet night coming, the glass is going
Down, the sun is going down.

LOUIS MACNEICE

King Foo Foo

Contents

King Foo Foo

King Foo Foo sat upon his throne
Dressed in his royal closes,
While all around his courtiers stood
With clothes-pegs on their noses.

'This action strange,' King Foo Foo said,
'My mind quite discomposes,
Though vulgar curiosity
A good king never shoses.'

But to the court it was as clear
As poetry or prose is:
King Foo Foo had not had a bath
Since goodness only knowses.

But one fine day the Fire Brigade
Rehearsing with their hoses
(To Handel's 'Water Music' played
With many puffs and bloses)

Quite failed the water to control
In all its ebbs and floses
And simply drenched the King with sev-
Eral thousand gallon doses.

At this each wight (though impolite)
A mighty grin exposes.
'At last,' the King said, 'now I see
That all my court morose is!

'A debt to keep his courtiers gay
A monarch surely owses,
And deep within my royal breast
A sporting heart reposes.'

So now each night its water bright
The Fire Brigade disposes
Over a King who smells as sweet
As all the royal roses.

CHARLES CAUSLEY

Evening Schoolboys

Hearken to that happy shout—the schoolhouse door
Is open thrown, and out the youngsters teem;
Some run to leapfrog on the rushy moor,
And others dabble in the shallow stream,
Catching young fish and turning pebbles o'er
For mussel clams. Look in that mellow gleam
Where the retiring sun that rests the while
Streams through the broken hedge. How happy seem
Those schoolboy friendships leaning o'er the stile,
Both reading in one book; anon a dream
Rich with new joys doth their young hearts beguile,
And the book's pocketed most hastily.
Ah, happy boys, well may ye turn and smile,
When joys are yours that never cost a sigh.

JOHN CLARE

I've Been Wandering in the Greenwoods

I've been wandering in the greenwoods,
And 'mid flowery, smiling plains;
I've been listening to the dark floods,
To the thrush's thrilling strains.

I have gathered the pale primrose,
And the purple violet sweet;
I've been where the asphodel grows,
And where lives the red deer fleet.

I've been to the distant mountain,
To the silver singing rill,
By the crystal murmuring fountain,
And the shady, verdant hill.

I've been where the poplar is springing
From the fair enamelled ground,
Where the nightingale is singing
With a solemn, plaintive sound.

EMILY BRONTË

Ruthless Rhyme Two

'There's been an accident!' they said,
'Your servant's cut in half; he's dead!'
'Indeed!' said Mr Jones, 'and please
Send me the half that's got my keys.'

HARRY GRAHAM

On a Quay by the Sea

On a quay by the sea
with one hand on his knee
sat Skipper ('Double D.') Dhu,
resting his eyes on
the far horizon
for want of something to do.

Up and up like a cup
that can sip its own sup
rose the tides of the turbulent sea,
but gravely he sat
gazing over, not at,
the monsters that gnashed at his knee.

The whales lashed their tails
like terrible flails
and the shark clashed its portcullis jaw;
round and round by the jetty
like a lot of spaghetti
the octopus rose with a roar.

Dhu sits and he knits
his brow as befits
a Captain among such a welter;
then he lowers his eye
and all of them fly
down to Davy Jones' Locker for shelter.

GEORGE BARKER

Night Clouds

The white mares of the moon rush along the sky
Beating their golden hoofs upon the glass Heavens;
The white mares of the moon are all standing on their hind legs
Pawing at the green porcelain doors of the remote Heavens.
Fly, mares!
Strain your utmost,
Scatter the milky dust of stars,
Or the tiger sun will leap upon you and destroy you
With one lick of his vermilion tongue.

AMY LOWELL .

The Swapping Song

O when I was a little boy I lived by myself
And all the bread and cheese I got I laid them on the shelf.
Tum a wing waw waddle tum a Jack straw straddle,
Tum a John paw faddle tum a long way home.

The rats and the mice they gave me such a life
I had to go to London to get me a wife.

The roads were so long and the streets were so narrow,
I had to bring her home in an old wheel-barrow.

My foot it slipped and I got a fall
And down went the wheel-barrow, wife and all.

I swapped my wheel-barrow and got me a horse
And then I rode from cross to cross.

I swapped my horse and got me a mare
And then I rode from fair to fair.

I swapped my mare and got me a cow
And in that trade I just learned how.

I swapped my cow and got me a calf
And in that trade I just lost half.

I swapped my calf and got me a mule
And then I rode like a doggone fool.

I swapped my mule and got me a sheep
And then I rode myself to sleep.

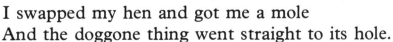

I swapped my sheep and got me a hen
And see what a pretty thing I had then.

I swapped my hen and got me a mole
And the doggone thing went straight to its hole.

AMERICAN FOLK SONG

First Dip

Wave after wavelet goes
Coldly over your toes
And sinks down into the stones.
Another mounts to your knees,
Icy, as if to freeze
Flesh and marrow and bones.
And now another, a higher,
Yellow with foam, and dire
With weed from yesterday's storm.
With a gasp you greet it—
Your shoulders stoop to meet it—
And you find ... you find ...
   Ah-h-h-h!
You find that the water's warm!

JOHN WALSH

The Redbreast

Like a reddish leaf
of green and brown,
the robin in the falling snow
flies up and down.

From the coalhouse to the tub,
the pantry to the byre,
closer he flies, and brings
his little panting fire.

He hops through the wind
of flakes, flits in a trice
from step to kitchen window,
pecks its crystal ice.

His eyes are big and cheeky,
black in his tilted head.
Shanks flexed for flight,
he begs a crumb of bread.

He chose our dark and stony yard
to warble long and loud.
—Why has he made us his?
Why do we feel so proud?

JAMES KIRKUP

Apples

Behold the apples' rounded worlds:
juice-green of July rain,
the black polestar of flower, the rind
mapped with its crimson stain.

The russet, crab and cottage red
burn to the sun's hot brass,
then drop like sweat from every branch
and bubble in the grass.

They lie as wanton as they fall,
and where they fall and break,
the stallion clamps his crunching jaws,
the starling stabs his beak.

In each plump gourd the cidery bite
of boys' teeth tears the skin;
the waltzing wasp consumes his share,
the bent worm enters in.

I, with an easy hunger, take
entire my season's dole;
welcome the ripe, the sweet, the sour,
the hollow and the whole.

LAURIE LEE

Three Cheers for the Black, White and Blue

Johnny is a long-haired Blue,
Looks a gentleman to you.
But his Ma was black and white,
Loved a dustbin, loved a fight;
And her little orphan boy,
Dressed up à la Fauntleroy,
Brushed and combed to look the part,
Has a wicked alley heart;
Swipes a titbit, smites a foe
With a fierce and expert blow;
Hands a deadly sock to those
Who interfere with his repose;
Circles round, intent to slog
Any inoffensive dog;
Is profuse in phrases terse

And turns a ready, witty curse.
Yet he's a taking little brute,
The Bruiser in his ritzy suit.

RUTH PITTER

A Dream of Winter

These flowers survive their lover bees,
    Whose deep bass voices filled the air;
The cuckoo and the nightingale
    Have come and gone, we know not where.

Now, in this green and silent world,
    In Autumn, full of smiling light,
I hear a bird that, suddenly,
    Startles my hearing and my sight.

It is the Robin, singing of
    A silver world of snow and frost;
Where all is cold and white—except
    The fire that's on his own warm breast.

W. H. DAVIES

The Duck and the Kangaroo

Said the Duck to the Kangaroo,
  'Good gracious, how you hop!
Over the fields and the water too,
  As if you would never stop!
My life is a bore in this nasty pond,
And I long to go out in the world beyond!
  I wish I could hop like you!'
  Said the Duck to the Kangaroo.

'Please give me a ride on your back!'
  Said the Duck to the Kangaroo.
'I would sit quite still, and say nothing but "Quack",
  The whole of the long day through!
And we'd go to the Dee, and the Jelly Bo Lee,
Over the land, and over the sea;—
  Please take me a ride! O do!'
  Said the Duck to the Kangaroo.

Said the Kangaroo to the Duck,
  'This requires some little reflection;
Perhaps on the whole it might bring me luck,
  And there seems but one objection,
Which is, if you'll let me speak so bold,
Your feet are unpleasantly wet and cold,
  And would probably give me the roo-
  Matiz!' said the Kangaroo.

Said the Duck, 'As I sate on the rocks,
  I have thought over that completely,
And I bought four pairs of worsted socks
  Which fit my web-feet neatly.
And to keep out the cold I've bought a cloak,
And every day a cigar I'll smoke,
  All to follow my own dear true
  Love of a Kangaroo!'

Said the Kangaroo, 'I'm ready!
  All in the moonlight pale;
But to balance me well, dear Duck, sit steady!
  And quite at the end of my tail!'
So away they went with a hop and a bound,
And they hopped the whole world three times round;
  And who so happy,—O who,
  As the Duck and the Kangaroo?

EDWARD LEAR

Pebbles

They lie on shores, margins of streams,
Pebbles, thousands, not one the same.
Veined, coloured, wave-worn,
They shine in shingle beds, through clear water,
Littered on curved beaches, dead jewels.
Began with raw rocks, high cliffs,
Tottering in air, battered by wild seas,
Slow rain, ice in crannies, the bursting root,
Long tides rolling them over and over,
Chiming against each other, the knock of the swell.
I hold a few in warm hands,
Fingers rejoicing in their smooth shapes,
Basalt and flint, granite, the strange serpentine;
And some have a crystal beauty,
Agate, cornelian, the midnight jet.
I love them, these stones,
Press them to my live cheeks,
Feel their dumb cold, hear far-off
The distant roar and grinding of old tides,
Time's ebb and flow, for ever and for ever.

LEONARD CLARK

The Hen and the Carp

Once, in a roostery,
there lived a speckled hen, and when-
ever she laid an egg this hen
    ecstatically cried:
'O progeny miraculous, particular spectaculous,
    what a wonderful hen am I!'

Down in a pond near by
perchance a gross and broody carp
was basking, but her ears were sharp—
    she heard Dame Cackle cry:
'O progeny miraculous, particular spectaculous,
    what a wonderful hen am I!'

'Ah, Cackle,' bubbled she,
'for your single egg, O silly one,
I lay at least a million;
    suppose for each I cried:
"O progeny miraculous, particular spectaculous!"
    what a hullaballoo there'd be!'

IAN SERRAILLIER

Ruthless Rhyme Three

Bob was bathing in the Bay,
When a Shark who passed that way
Punctured him in seven places;
—And he made *such* funny faces!

HARRY GRAHAM

The Shepherd Boy

The shepherd boy a kingdom rules,
  An emerald hill his throne;
Crown'd with golden sunshine,
  He reigneth there alone.

His goats, court-players are;
  Each wears a tinkling bell,
And the birds' sweet pipings,
  A royal concert tell.

And the piping and the bells,
   With the brook's soft rhymes,
Lull the drowsy king to sleep,
   While gently nod the pines.

HEINRICH HEINE

The Ballad of the Carpenters

An ancient woman met with me,
Her voice was silver as her hair,
Her wild black eyes were certainly
The strangest I have seen.
She told a tale of carpenters
Who laboured for a queen.

'I had an island in a lake
A wide lake, a quiet lake
Of sweet security.
I called them to me by the lake,
And they came gladly for my sake,
My seven singing carpenters,
To build a house for me.

'They brought the hammers and the nails,
The pegs, the twine, the chisel blade,
The saw and whizzing plane.
They brought good share of timber wood,
Of resin wood, sweet smelling wood
Split kindly to the grain.
They brought them all for love of me;
They did not seek for gain.

'They built a house of singing wood,
The white wood, the splendid wood,
And made it snug around.
Their hammers on the ringing wood
Made all the lake resound.

'The tench stirred dimly in his dream,
The glowing carp, the silly bream
Could hear the muffled sound.

'But someone grudged the fragrant wood
And sent a storm upon my house,
A black flood, a silver flood
Of wind and stinging rain.
The waters writhed in hissing rage,
The yelling wind, the rain-pocked waves
Rose in a hurricane.

'The slaty waves foamed hillock high,
The thunder pranced about the sky,
The lightning's bare and crooked fang
Gleamed where the cloud-lip curled.

'And when the calm came and the peace
Of wind's cease and water's cease,
My house and seven carpenters
Had vanished from the world.'

L. A. G. STRONG

from The Task

Forth goes the woodman, leaving unconcerned
The cheerful haunts of man, to wield the axe,
And drive the wedge in yonder forest drear,
From morn to eve his solitary task.
Shaggy and lean, and shrewd, with pointed ears
And tail cropped short, half lurcher and half cur,
His dog attends him. Close behind his heel
Now creeps he slow; and now, with many a frisk
Wide scampering, snatches up the drifted snow
With ivory teeth, or ploughs it with his snout;
Then shakes his powdered coat, and barks for joy.
Heedless of all his pranks, the sturdy churl
Moves right towards the mark; nor stops for aught,
But, now and then, with pressure of his thumb
To adjust the fragrant charge of a short tube,
That fumes beneath his nose: the trailing cloud
Streams far behind him, scenting all the air.
Now from the roost, or from the neighbouring pale,
Where diligent to catch the first faint gleam
Of smiling day, they gossiped side by side,
Come trooping at the housewife's well-known call

The feathered tribe domestic. Half on wing
And half on foot, they brush the fleecy wood,
Conscious, and fearful of too deep a plunge.
The sparrows peep, and quit the sheltering eaves,
To seize the fair occasion. Well they eye
The scattered grain, and thievishly resolve
To escape the impending famine, often scared
As oft return, a pert voracious kind.

WILLIAM COWPER

The Derby Ram

As I was going to Derby, sir,
Upon a market day,
I saw the biggest ram, sir,
That ever was fed on hay.

And indeed, sir, 'tis true, sir,
I never was given to lie,
And if you'd been to Derby, sir,
You'd have seen him as well as I.

This ram was fat behind, sir,
This ram was fat before;
He measured ten yards round, sir,
If not a little more.

He had four feet to walk on, sir,
He had four feet to stand,
And every foot he had, sir,
Did cover an acre of land.

The man who killed this ram, sir,
Was drowned in all the blood,
And he who held the dish, sir,
Was carried away in the flood.

The mutton that ram made, sir,
Gave all the Army meat,
And what was left, I'm told, sir,
Was served out to the Fleet.

The wool grew on his back, sir,
It reached up to the sky,
And there the eagles built their nests,
I heard the young ones cry.

The wool grew on his belly, sir,
It reached down to the ground,
And that was sold in Derby town
For forty thousand pound.

The horns upon this ram, sir,
They reached up to the moon.
A little boy went up in January,
And he never got back till June.

And all the boys of Derby
Came begging for his eyes,
To make themselves some footballs,
For they were of football size.

TRADITIONAL

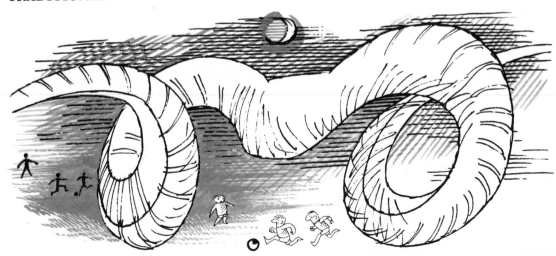

56

Warning

When I am an old woman I shall wear purple
With a red hat that doesn't go, and doesn't suit me,
And I shall spend my pension on brandy and summer gloves
And satin sandals, and say we've no money for butter.
I shall sit down on the pavement when I'm tired
And gobble up samples in shops and press alarm bells
And run my stick along the public railings
And make up for the sobriety of my youth.
I shall go out in my slippers in the rain
And pick the flowers in other people's gardens
And learn to spit.

You can wear terrible shirts and grow more fat
And eat three pounds of sausages at a go
Or only bread and pickles for a week
And hoard pens and pencils and beermats and things in boxes.

But now we must have clothes that keep us dry
And pay our rent and not swear in the street
And set a good example for the children.
We will have friends to dinner and read the papers.

But maybe I ought to practise a little now?
So people who know me are not too shocked and surprised
When suddenly I am old and start to wear purple.

JENNY JOSEPH

Follower

My father worked with a horse-plough,
His shoulders globed like a full sail strung
Between the shafts and the furrow.
The horses strained at his clicking tongue.

An expert. He would set the wing
And fit the bright steel-pointed sock.
The sod rolled over without breaking.
At the headrig, with a single pluck

Of reins, the sweating team turned round
And back into the land. His eye
Narrowed and angled at the ground,
Mapping the furrow exactly.

I stumbled in his hob-nailed wake,
Fell sometimes on the polished sod;
Sometimes he rode me on his back
Dipping and rising to his plod.

I wanted to grow up and plough,
To close one eye, stiffen my arm.
All I ever did was follow
In his broad shadow round the farm.

I was a nuisance, tripping, falling,
Yapping always. But today
It is my father who keeps stumbling
Behind me, and will not go away.

SEAMUS HEANEY

Night Fears

Curled closely in his little bed
  He lay and watched the last thin light
Dwindle to darkness; then once more dread
  Tapped at his window with the night.

Outside, the voices of the rain
  Whimpered and chuckled; he could hear
A cat scream like a thing in pain,
  Some waiting wind-tossed shape of fear

Lost in the darkness ... Suddenly
  A chair creaked in the goblin-pit
They called a room by day, and he
  Felt his heart leap at sound of it.

Was it a chair? and nothing more?
  Suppose some leering long dead man—
With desperate small hands he tore
  The bedclothes from his face and ran.

The ogre fingers of the night
  Clutched at him from the walls and floor,
Till stumbling, sobbing, blind with fright,
  He found somehow his prison door

And flung it wide. The light that burned
  Sentinel in the passage way
Leaped shouting in the room and turned
  The hideous night to lovely day.

BRIAN HILL

Fishers

That Sunday morning, the moon still high
over the town, blessing the lapping water,
we left the harbour mouth in Peter's boat,
rounded the point, then steered
for the open sea, engines
purring like contented cats.
A steady five knots we made, were well out
in the grounds by sunrise, gulls following,
a white cloud of witnesses.

Sleep in our eyes we dropped nets, trawled
an hour or so, the wind keen,
it seemed we had no hands.
We landed mackerel twice from a small shoal,
a few dabs, a dogfish or two,
nothing to boast about, but a fair catch.
By seven the moon had gone, the sun
stroked sea and sky, there was no swell;
we tried again, no fish, decided to return,
breakfast waiting at home, the family fire.

Then Peter spotted something in the net
we had not bargained for, an old iron chest,
deeper than long, rounded at the top,
rusted and green, bound with two clasps.
Andrew, our skipper, laid it on the deck,
swimming with water and scales, we stared,
wondering what the strange box held;
we forgot the fish in the hold, the wind
salting our skins, our eyes
sharp as diamonds.

The keyhole was stopped with mud, broken shell,
the clasps soon gave, the lock held fast;
Peter broke it with a gutting knife,
gasped, raised his eyes to heaven,
lifted out two plates,
tarnished by time, a burnished cup
with delicate, figured stem,
and last, a jewelled crucifix,
that glittered in the first-day sun,
ruby and amethyst, a holy sight.
Then Peter raised the cross on high,
we had no words, but thought
we heard church bells on the land,
ringing for early service. Turned about,
chugged back home.

It was a nine days' wonder,
we told the tale a hundred times,
though Andrew kept his peace;
Peter only smiled
when people questioned him.
We later learned the silver and the gold
were Mexican, the treasure we had found,
from a great galleon, wrecked
upon our needle coasts, intended
for some English church by priests
who sailed with that proud fleet
and longed to hear the Mass said once again.

Now above the altar of our church
the jewelled cross shines, the cup and plates
are used, the old faith with the new.

LEONARD CLARK

How to Paint the Portrait of a Bird

First paint a cage
with an open door
then paint
something pretty
something simple
something fine
something useful
for the bird
next place the canvas against a tree
in a garden
in a wood
or in a forest
hide behind the tree
without speaking
without moving . . .

Sometimes the bird comes quickly
but it can also take many years
before making up its mind
Don't be discouraged
wait
wait if necessary for years
the quickness or the slowness of the coming
of the bird having no relation
to the success of the picture
When the bird comes
if it comes
observe the deepest silence
wait for the bird to enter the cage
and when it has entered
gently close the door with the paint-brush
then
one by one paint out all the bars
taking care not to touch one feather of the bird
Next make a portrait of the tree
choosing the finest of its branches
for the bird
Paint also the green leaves and the freshness of the wind
dust in the sun
and the sound of the grazing cattle in the heat of summer
and wait for the bird to decide to sing
if the bird does not sing
it is a bad sign
a sign that the picture is bad
but if it sings it is a good sign
a sign that you are ready to sign
so then you pluck very gently
one of the quills of the bird
and you write your name in the corner of the picture.

JACQUES PREVERT
(Translated from the French by Paul Dehn)

Approach of Spring

Now that the winter's gone, the earth hath lost
Her snow-white robes, and now no more the frost
Candies the grass, or calls an icy cream
Upon the silver lake, or crystal stream;
But the warm sun thaws the benumb'd earth,
And makes it tender; gives a second birth
To the dead swallow; wakes in hollow tree
The drowsy cuckoo, and the humble bee;
Now do a choir of chirping minstrels bring
In triumph to the world the youthful Spring.

THOMAS CAREW

Go, Pretty Child

Go, pretty child, and bear this flower
Unto thy little saviour;
And tell Him, by that bud now blown,
He is the Rose of Sharon known:
When thou hast said so, stick it there
Upon his bib, or stomacher:
And tell Him, for good hansel too,
That thou hast brought a whistle new,
Made of clean straight oaten reed,
To charm his cries, at time of need:
Tell Him, for coral, thou hast none:
But if thou hadst, He should have one;
But poor thou art, and known to be
Even as moneyless, as He.
Lastly, if thou canst win a kiss
From those mellifluous lips of His;
Then never take a second one
To spoil the first impression.

ROBERT HERRICK

64

The Flattered Flying Fish

Contents

The Flattered Flying Fish

Said the Shark to the Flying Fish over the phone:
'Will you join me tonight? I am dining alone.
Let me order a nice little dinner for two!
And come as you are, in your shimmering blue.'

Said the Flying Fish: 'Fancy remembering me,
And the dress that I wore at the Porpoises' tea!'
'How could I forget?' said the Shark in his guile:
'I expect you at eight!' and rang off with a smile.

She has powdered her nose; she has put on her things;
She is off with one flap of her luminous wings.
O little one, lovely, light-hearted and vain,
The Moon will not shine on your beauty again!

E. V. RIEU

Apartment Cats

The Girls wake, stretch, and pad up to the door.
    They rub my leg and purr:
    One sniffs around my shoe,
    Rich with an outside smell.
  The other rolls back on the floor—
White bib exposed, and stomach of soft fur.

Now, more awake, they re-enact Ben Hur
    Along the corridor,
        Wheel, gallop; as they do,
        Their noses twitching still,
    Their eyes get wild, their bodies tense,
Their usual prudence seemingly withdraws.

And then they wrestle: parry, lock of paws,
    Blind hug of close defence,
        Tail-thump, and smothered mew.
        If either, though, feel claws,
    She abruptly rises, knowing well
How to stalk off in wise indifference.

THOM GUNN

The Monster

A monster who lives in Loch Ness
Is ten thousand years old, more or less:
    He's asleep all the time—
    Which is hardly a crime:
If he weren't, we'd be in a mess.

EDWARD LOWBURY

House of Sand

We knew it wouldn't last. That's why
We thumbed in turrets so prettily, fashioned doors
And windows, too, for small sand people to come

In and go out again—our little house,
Dark damp sand, driveway scored in, the sea
Encroaching upon our play.

   We watched it fall
Prey to grey water swirling, helped it on
With a good boot or two, stood by and smiled—

Our house of sand melts to a shapeless mound.

PHILIP HOBSBAUM

Ruthless Rhyme Four

O'er the rugged mountain's brow
Clara threw the twins she nursed,
And remarked, 'I wonder now
which will reach the bottom first?'

HARRY GRAHAM

A Garden at Night

On powdery wings the white moths pass,
And petals fall on the dewy grass;
Over the bed where the poppy sleeps
The furtive fragrance of lavender creeps.
Here lived an old lady in days long gone,
And the ghost of that lady lingers on.
She sniffs the roses, and seems to see
The ripening fruit on the orchard tree;
Like the scent of flowers her spirit weaves
Its winding way through the maze of leaves;
Up and down like the moths it goes:
Never and never it finds repose.
Gentle she was, and quiet and kind,
But flitting and restless was her old mind.
So hither and thither across the lawn
Her spirit wanders, till grey of dawn
Rouses the cock in the valley far,
And the garden waits for the morning star.

JAMES REEVES

Kiph

My Uncle Ben, who's been
To Bisk, Bhir, Biak—
Been, and come back:
To Tab, Tau, Tze, and Tomsk,
And home, by Teneriffe:
Who, brown as desert sand,
Gaunt, staring, slow, and stiff,
Has chased the Unicorn
And Hippogriff,
Gave me a smooth, small, shining stone,
Called *Kiph*.

'Look'ee, now, Nevvy mine,'
He told me—'*If*
You'd wish a wish,
Just rub this smooth, small, shining stone,
Called *Kiph*.'

Hid it did I,
In a safe, secret spot;
Slept, and the place
In dreams forgot.

One wish *alone*
Now's mine: Oh, if
I could but find again
That stone called *Kiph*!

WALTER DE LA MARE

from **Reynard the Fox**

At Ghost Heath Wood on Ghost Heath Down,
The hounds went crackling through the brown
Dry stalks of bracken killed by frost.

The fox's nose tipped up and round,
Since smell is a part of sight and sound.
His ears were cocked and his keen nose flaired,
He sneered with his lips till his teeth were bared.

On Ghost Heath turf was a steady drumming
Which sounded like horses quickly coming,
And another noise, of a pit-pat beat
On the Ghost Hill grass, of foxhound feet.

Then the wood-end rang with a clear voice crying,
And the cackle of scrub where hounds were trying.
Then the horn blew nearer, a hound's voice quivered,
Then another, then more, till his body shivered.

The sound of the nearness sent a flood
Of terror of death through the fox's blood.
He upped his brush and he cocked his nose,
And he went upwind as a racer goes.

Then again the kettledrum horsehooves beat,
And the green blades bent to the fox's feet,
And the cry rose keen not far behind
Of the 'Blood, blood, blood', in the foxhounds' mind.

At the sixth green field came the long slow climb
To the Mourne End Wood, as old as time;
Dark woods evil, but burrowed deep
With a brock's earth strong, where a fox might sleep.

He was all one ache, one gasp, one thirsting,
Heart on his chest-bones, beating, bursting;
The hounds were gaining like spotted pards,
And the wood edge still was a hundred yards.

He gathered himself, he leaped, he reached
The top of the hedge like a fish-boat beached.
He steadied a second and then leaped down
To the dark of the wood where bright things drown.

He crossed the covert, he crawled the bank,
To a meuse in the thorns, and there he sank,
With his ears flexed back and his teeth shown white,
In a rat's resolve for a dying bite.

After an hour no riders came,
The day drew by like an ending game;
A robin sang from a pufft red breast,
The fox lay quiet and took his rest.

The stars grew bright as the yews grew black,
The fox rose stiffly and stretched his back.
He flaired the air, then he padded out
To the valley below him, dark as doubt.

Then the moon came quiet and flooded full
Light and beauty on clouds like wool,
On a feasted fox at rest from hunting,
In the beechwood grey where the brocks were grunting.

JOHN MASEFIELD

The Ghosts' High Noon

When the night wind howls in the chimney cowls, and
    the bat in the moonlight flies,
And inky clouds, like funeral shrouds, sail over the
    midnight skies—
When the footpads quail at the night-bird's wail, and
    black dogs bay the moon,
Then is the spectres' holiday—then is the ghosts' high noon!

As the sob of the breeze sweeps over the trees, and the
    mists lie low on the fen,
From grey tombstones are gathered the bones that once
    were women and men,
And away they go, with a mop and a mow, to the revel
    that ends too soon,
For cockcrow limits our holiday—the dead of the night's
    high noon!

And then each ghost with his ladye-toast to their church-
    yard beds take flight,
With a kiss, perhaps, on her lantern chaps, and a grisly
    grim 'good night';
Till the welcome knell of the midnight bell rings forth its
    jolliest tune,
And ushers our next high holiday—the dead of the night's
    high noon!

W. S. GILBERT

What's Little Babies Made Of?

What's old women made of, made of?
What's old women made of?
Reels and jeels and old spinning-wheels,
And that's what old women are made of.

What's old men made of, made of?
What's old men made of?
Whisky and brandy and sugar and candy,
And that's what old men are made of.

What's young women made of, made of?
What's young women made of?
Rings and jings and all fine things,
And that's what young women are made of

What's little boys made of, made of?
What's little boys made of?
Piggins and pails and puppy dogs' tails,
And that's what little boys are made of.

What's little babies made of, made of?
What's little babies made of?
Cookies and crumbs and sweet sugar plums,
And that's what little babies are made of.

AMERICAN FOLK SONG

Fetching Cows

The black one, last as usual, swings her head
And coils a black tongue round a grass-tuft. I
Watch her soft weight come down, her split feet spread.

In front, the others swing and slouch; they roll
Their great Greek eyes and breathe out milky gusts
From muzzles black and shiny as wet coal.

The collie trots, at my heels, then plops
Into the ditch. The sea makes a tired sound
That's always stopping though it never stops.

A haycart squats prickeared against the sky,
Hay breath and milk breath. Far out in the West
The wrecked sun founders though its colours fly.

The collie's bored. There's nothing to control ...
The black cow is two native carriers
Bringing its belly home, slung from a pole.

NORMAN MACCAIG

I Wonder What it Feels Like to be Drowned?

Look at my knees,
That island rising from the stormy seas!
The candle's a tall lightship; my two hands
Are boats and barges anchored to the sands,
With mighty cliffs all round:
They're full of wine and riches from far lands ...
I wonder what it feels like to be drowned?

I can make caves,
By lifting up the island and huge waves
And storms, and then with head and ears well under
Blow bubbles with a monstrous roar like thunder,
A Bull-of-Bashan sound.
The seas run high and the boats split asunder . . .
I wonder what it feels like to be drowned?

The thin soap slips
And slithers like a shark under the ships.
My toes are on the soap-dish—that's the effect
Of my huge storms; an iron steamer's wrecked.
The soap slides round and round;
He's biting the old sailors, I expect . . .
I wonder what it feels like to be drowned?

ROBERT GRAVES

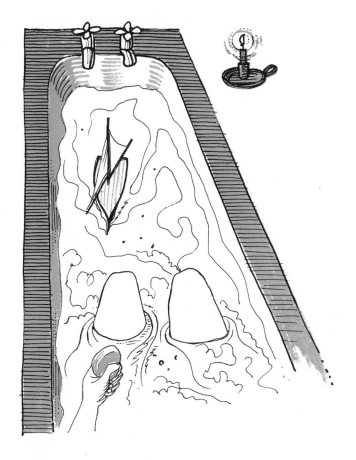

Boy and Fish

The sun is bright and clear, fish.

       Thank you, we can see it, boy.

The sand is soft and warm, fish.

       We don't care a bit, boy.

My feet are making rings, fish.

       We can make them, too, boy.

I'm looking hard at you, fish.

       We're looking hard at you, boy.

I have a little net, fish.

       So that's your little plan, boy.

I'm going to catch you now, fish.

       Well, catch us if you can, boy.

I have my bucket here, fish.

       Then fill it to the top, boy.

There's room for all of you, fish.

       We cannot really stop, boy.

Tomorrow I'll be back, fish.

       Tomorrow we'll be here, boy.

I'll have another try, fish.

       The sun is bright and clear, boy.

LEONARD CLARK

Parrot

Sometimes I sit with both eyes closed,
But all the same, I've heard!
They're saying, 'He won't talk because
He is a *thinking* bird.'

I'm olive-green and sulky, and
The Family say, 'Oh yes,
He's silent, but he's *listening*,
He *thinks* more than he *says*!

'He ponders on the things he hears,
Preferring not to chatter.'
—And this is true, but *why* it's true
Is quite another matter.

I'm working out some shocking things
In order to surprise them,
And when my thoughts are ready I'll
Certainly *not* disguise them!

I'll wait, and see, and choose a time
When everyone is present,
And clear my throat and raise my beak
And give a squawk and start to speak
And go on for about a week
And it will not be pleasant!

ALAN BROWNJOHN

Goodbat Nightman

God bless all policemen
and fighters of crime,
May thieves go to jail
for a very long time.

They've had a hard day
helping clean up the town,
Now they hang from the mantelpiece
both upside down.

A glass of warm blood
and then straight up the stairs,
Batman and Robin
Are saying their prayers.

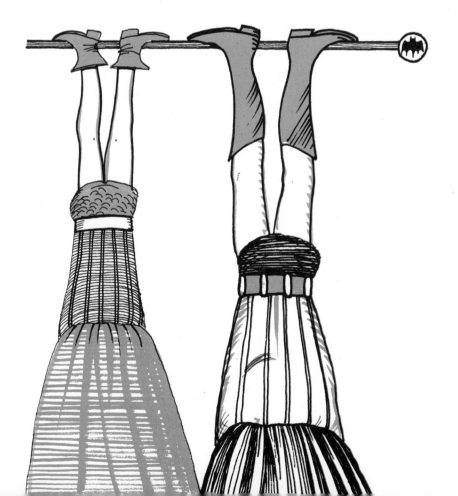

They've locked all the doors
and they've put out the bat,
Put on their batjamas
(They like doing that).

They've filled their batwater-bottles,
made their batbeds,
With two springy battresses
for sleepy batheads.

They're closing red eyes
and they're counting black sheep,
Batman and Robin
are falling asleep.

ROGER MCGOUGH

The Song of Seven

Far away, and long ago—
May sweet Memory be forgiven!
Came a Wizard in the evening,
And he sang the Song of Seven.
Yes, he plucked his jangling harp-strings
With fingers smooth and even;
And his eyes beneath his dangling hair
Were still as is the sea;
But the Song of Seven has never yet,
One note, come back to me.

The Song of One I know,
A rose its thorns between;

The Song of Two I learned
Where only the birds have been;

The Song of Three I heard
When March was fleet with hares;

The Song of Four was the wind's—the wind's,
Where wheat grew thick with tares;

The Song of Five, ah me!
Lovely the midmost one;

The Song of Six died out
Before the dream was done ...

One—two—three—four—five, six—
And all the grace notes given:
But *widdershins*, and witchery-sweet,
Where is the Song of Seven?

WALTER DE LA MARE

83

The Storm

The garden looks like its own photograph;
No leaf moves; the day holds its breath
And grows so dark and still,
We think it's dead—or taken strangely ill,
Feverish, with a hot, dry sky,
A hectic glow, a film over its eye.
The slightest sound is startling—whispers, buzzing flies.

But then, as night arrives, the storm breaks:
Light flickers over drenched roofs, rocks;
The sky is lit, as though
Day had returned—or perhaps the ghost of day;
A white whip cracks over our heads, and thunder
Drowns every other sound.... But then, a wonder:
The fever drops, and day looks out from open eyes!

EDWARD LOWBURY

A shadow is floating through the moonlight

A shadow is floating through the moonlight.
Its wings don't make a sound.
Its claws are long, its beak is bright.
Its eyes try all the corners of the night.

It calls and calls: all the air swells and heaves
And washes up and down like water.
The ear that listens to the owl believes
In death. The bat beneath the eaves,

The mouse beside the stone are still as death.
The owl's air washes them like water.
The owl goes back and forth inside the night,
And the night holds its breath.

RANDALL JARRELL

The Riddles of Christmas

How can a boy
Be king, yet lie in a manger?

How can a child be loved,
Yet die as a stranger?

How can he hansel the gifts
Of kings, and yet be poor?

How can his life
Be brief, and yet endure?

How can there hang a star
Where none blazed in the sky?

How can a man
Be born, yet never die?

Who is this stranger comes
As if he knew us all our days?

Who is this child of man
Clothed in the light of space?

Answer is there none
But Christ, the All, the One?

JAMES KIRKUP

Words for the Embroidered Hanging of His Bed

The wind's on the wold
And the night is a-cold,
And Thames runs chill
'Twixt mead and hill.
But kind and dear
Is the old house here
And my heart is warm
'Midst Winter's harm.
Rest then and rest,
And think of the best
'Twixt summer and spring,
When all birds sing
In the town of the tree,
And ye lie in me
And scarce dare move
Lest earth and its love
Should fade away
Ere the full of the day.
I am old and have seen
Many things that have been;
Both grief and peace
And wane and increase.
No tale I tell
Of ill or well,
But this I say,
Night treadeth on day,
And for worst and best
Right good is rest.

WILLIAM MORRIS

Ruthless Rhyme Five

Father heard his children scream,
So he threw them in the stream,
Saying, as he dropped the third,
'Children should be seen, not heard.'

HARRY GRAHAM

The Squirrel

We watched the old man carving; his fingers moved
The delicate tools upon the crimson wood.
In the dark of the crowded little workroom
We followed his fingers and, breathless, leaned and stood,
Till out of the jumble of nails and hammers and saws,
In the little room, he held in his hands a squirrel,
With crimson fur, bright eyes, a nut in its paws.

SYLVIA READ

Romance

When I was but thirteen or so
  I went into a golden land;
Chimborazo, Cotopaxi
  Took me by the hand.

My father died, my brother too,
  They passed like fleeting dreams.
I stood where Popocatapetl
  In the sunlight gleams.

I dimly heard the master's voice
  And boys far off at play.
Chimborazo, Cotopaxi
  Had stolen me away.

I walked in a great golden dream
  To and fro from school—
Shining Popocatapetl
  The dusty streets did rule.

I walked home with a gold dark boy,
  And never a word I'd say,
Chimborazo, Cotopaxi
  Had taken my speech away:

I gazed entranced upon his face
  Fairer than any flower—
O shining Popocatapetl,
  It was thy magic hour:

The houses, people, traffic seemed
  Thin fading dreams by day,
Chimborazo, Cotopaxi
  They had stolen my soul away.

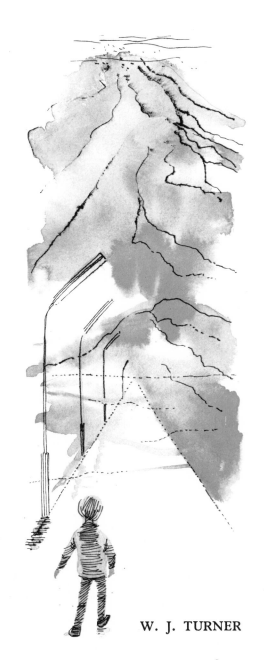

W. J. TURNER

from The Farmer's Boy

The clatt'ring Dairy-Maid, immers'd in steam,
Singing and scrubbing midst her milk and cream,
Bawls out, 'Go fetch the Cows!' ... Giles hears no more;
For pigs, and ducks, and turkeys, throng the door,
And sitting hens, for constant war prepar'd;
A concert strange to that which late he heard.
Straight to the meadow then he whistling goes;
With well-known halloo calls his lazy Cows.
Forth comes the Maid, and like the morning smiles;
The Mistress too, and followed close by Giles.
A friendly tripod forms their humble seat,
With pails bright scour'd, and delicately sweet.
Where shadowing elms obstruct the morning ray,
Begins the work, begins the simple lay;
The full-charg'd udder yields its willing streams,
While Mary sings some lover's amorous dreams;
And crouching Giles beneath a neighbouring tree
Tugs o'er his pail, and chants with equal glee.

With joy the Mistress views her plenteous reeking store,
And bears a brimmer to the dairy door;
And now the Dairy claims her choicest care,
And half her household find employment there:
Slow rolls the churn, its load of clogging cream
At once forgoes its quality and name;
From knotty particles first floating wide
Congealing butter's dash'd from side to side;
Streams of new milk through golden coolers stray,
And snow-white curd abounds, and wholesome whey.

ROBERT BLOOMFIELD

90

To My Sister

It is the first mild day of March:
Each minute sweeter than before,
The redbreast sings from the tall larch
That stands beside our door.

There is a blessing in the air,
Which seems a sense of joy to yield
To the bare trees, and mountains bare,
And grass in the green field.

My sister ('tis a wish of mine)
Now that our morning meal is done,
Make haste, your morning task resign;
Come forth and feel the sun.

Edward will come with you—and pray,
Put on with speed your woodland dress;
And bring no book: for this one day
We'll give to idleness.

WILLIAM WORDSWORTH

Brave Rover

Rover killed the goat,
He bit him through the throat,
And when it was all over
The goat's ghost haunted Rover.

And yet (the plot here thickens)
Rover killed the chickens.
They thought he was a fox—
And then he killed the cocks.

And now events move faster:
Rover killed his master,
And then he took the life
Of his late master's wife.

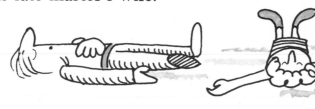

And we must not forget he
Killed Rachel and killed Bettie,
Then Billie and then John.
How dogs do carry on!

To Bradford he repaired.
His great white teeth he bared
And then, with awful snarls,
Polished off Uncle Charles.

Albert in London trembled—
An aspen he resembled—
His life he held not cheap
And wept. (I heard him weep.)

Brave Rover heard him too.
He knew full well who's who,
And entered with a grin
The Fields of Lincoln's Inn.

The Elysian Fields begin
Near those of Lincoln's Inn.
'Tis there that Albert's gone.
How dogs do carry on!

MAX BEERBOHM

The Old Field

The old field is sad
Now the children have gone home.
They have played with him all afternoon,
Kicking the ball to him, and him
Kicking it back.

But now it is growing cold and dark.
He thinks of their warm breath, and their
Feet like little hot-water bottles.
A bit rough, some of them, but still ...

And now, he thinks, there's not even a dog
To tickle me.
The gates are locked.
The birds don't like this nasty sneaking wind,
And nor does he.

D. J. ENRIGHT

Words for Singing

There was a bird all summer sang,
Winging its five white notes.
There was a bird all summer long
Singing the one bright song away,
La ti la fe ray.

It sang in the hawthorn and the briar,
Winging its five white notes,
It sang in the meadow and the mere,
Singing the one bright song away,
La ti la fe ray.

It sang last night as never before,
Winging its five white notes:
We shall never hear it more
Singing the one bright song away,
La ti la fe ray.

For the summer has come and gone away
Winging its five white notes:
We shall never again see the bleaching hay
Or hear the bird of yesterday
Singing the one bright song away,
La ti la fe ray.

JAMES KIRKUP

95

Carol

Until I wander'd through the world
   I did not know
That even in Bethlehem
   Falls the white snow.

Then I did imagine how
   A morning long ago
Reflected light from all the land
   Flooded through the door.

And lit the spidery rafters
   Above the sleeping child
Whose eyes were lifted up to
   A mother mild.

And such radiance was around
   On ass and munching cow
Some said because a child was born
   And some because of snow.

HERBERT READ

96